CARTOON CLASSICS

from
MEDICAL ECONOMICS

CARTOON CLASSICS
from
MEDICAL ECONOMICS

Medical Economics Book Division, Inc.
Oradell, New Jersey

"O.K. . . . So he wrote an oath and a couple of good papers. In private practice, he'd fall flat on his face."

"I don't think young Zackley there is going to make it."

Language specialist

While on grand ward rounds, the chief attending got interested in the case of an Italian patient and tried to elicit a further history from him. Unfortunately the man couldn't speak much English. Finally someone remembered there was an interne in the hospital who had the linguistic ability needed. So the chief sent for him posthaste.

The interne arrived and bustled importantly through the circle of doctors to act as interpreter. With the chief at his elbow, he approached the bedside. Then, in a loud voice, he shouted at the puzzled patient, "Hey, Joe! Whatsa matt'?"

— *James Robertson,* M.D.

"Fill 'er up!"

"You know that patient I was prepping for surgery? I think I <u>did</u> the surgery!"

"I'm scheduled for a medical checkup. See that I pass."

"A card."

The next voice you hear . . .

I was using the facilities of the university's OBG clinic to make some electromyographic studies of uterine motility. The psychiatry department had warned me that the machine wasn't too well-insulated but that it should serve my purpose. Anyway, I rigged up a set of special electrodes for attachment to the cervix and selected as my first subject a young country girl.

After getting the recording going, I stepped out into the corridor for a smoke. A moment later a shriek from the patient brought me back on the double. "Doctor," she quavered, "they're talking from my womb!"

The girl was obviously imagining things. But, to humor her, I bent over to listen. To my astonishment, a deep, muted voice emanating from her vulva announced, "Ladies and gentlemen, you are tuned to the Nation's Station."

— *N. S. Assali*, M.D.

"I don't know whether to call him John, Edward or William."

Jerry Marcus

Dead end

An elderly gentleman from deep in the Ozarks came to our cancer clinic. Covering the dorsum of one hand was an ulcerated, fungating carcinoma. One of the house staff said, "Grandpa, why in the world did you wait so long before you came to the doctor?"

Replied the ancient sage: "Well, son, I knowed this thing was a cancer. But I didn't see no need to hurry. It was already down agin the bone where it couldn't go no further."

— *Wilfred E. Woolridge*, M.D.

Special delivery

After examining a woman with a severely decompensated heart, I told her husband that she was seriously ill, that she would have to be hospitalized and that I'd send an ambulance for her. A couple of hours later at the hospital, the admitting clerk phoned me that the *husband* had arrived in the ambulance—without his wife. Puzzled, I asked to talk to him.

"Didn't you understand that the ambulance was sent out for your wife?" I said sternly. "Where is she?"

"We had an argument," he answered bleakly, "and she took the bus."
— *Nathan Flaxman*, M.D.

"I hadn't intended staying for dinner."

"I know the staff voted me the best secretary they ever had, but my office nurse says the work's killing her!"

Time for reflection

The patient, a young student in a watch repair school, had suffered head lacerations in an auto accident. In view of his circumstances, I set the fee for his several treatments at a nominal $10. On his second visit he cheerfully announced that his insurance company was paying the bill. But apparently feeling some further obligation, he asked if I had any watches that needed repairing. I gave him an old one that hadn't run for years.

On his last visit he presented me proudly with the watch—and a bill for $10. Flabbergasted, I endorsed over the insurance check and watched him depart, $10 richer and a well man. Then I glanced down at the watch in my hand. It had stopped. It hasn't run since.

— *Clifford A. Barber,* M.D.

"You have the same thing that my brother-in-law—Heaven rest his soul—had."

"I hate the blocks. But those ink spots send me."

"All I said was, 'What's burning for dinner?' "

Asking the impossible

Long before the days of tranquilizers, I had a woman patient who was a great worrier. I undertook to explain to her a method by which she could eventually stop worrying. To illustrate, I said:

"Suppose you yearn to play the piano. You must first learn the basic principles and then practice and practice. You will progress through the playing of simple music to more difficult pieces, and finally master highly complicated compositions. If your ambition is great enough, nothing will hold you from your ultimate aim of playing the piano as it should be played. The same basic procedure must be followed to overcome a bad habit like worrying. You must first learn the basic principles. Then you must practice them consistently."

As I sat back, she replied thoughtfully, "Well, maybe you're right, Doctor. But I just can't do it."

"Surely you can," I said. "Others have done it. You can, too."

"I'm afraid I can't," she demurred. "You see—we sold our piano last week."

— *Frank C. Metzger*, M.D.

Weaker sex

I'd just cauterized a bleeder on the nasal septum. The epistaxis had subsided, and I was standing idly by. Suddenly the patient—a plethoric, hypertensive white mountain of female fat—decided to hoist herself from the operating table into her wheel chair. What she used for a fulcrum was my shoulders.

The black spots still before my eyes, I said, "Good grief, Mrs. Porcino, you could have broken my back."

Could have, and did. Two days later an X-ray revealed a compression fracture of a dorsal vertebra. I'm still wearing a spinal brace—and staying away from overweight patients.

— *John Parker,* M.D.

"When he says, 'I'll bet you're the bravest boy on your block,' I say, 'No, but I can scream the loudest!'"

"I'm still a virgin. Are you?"

How's that again?

I'm a doctor's aide. The doctor asked me to get an old colleague of his on the phone. As I lifted the receiver to dial the number, I found an incoming call already on the line. It was one of our women patients.

She sounded urgent, so I put her through to the doctor at once. Thinking it was his old buddy, he picked up the phone and boomed, "Hello, you old sonofabitch! How in hell are you?"

— *Imogene Byrne*

"Look, Ma, a bank robber!"

Low man

The patient, about to have his chest X-rayed, was wearing a hand-painted necktie featuring a gaudy totem pole. The technician, a winsome thing, asked him to remove from his clothing any metallic object that might obscure the film. He discarded his tie clasp, fountain pen and pencil, then asked, "What about my totem pole? Will that get in the way?"

The girl was speechless with embarrassment until the patient, as an afterthought, pointed to his tie.

— *A. W. Squires*, M.D.

"I've got a warning for you; but keep it under your scrub cap:
The tissue committee has had the O.R. bugged."

"Perhaps you're not trying hard enough."

"How's that nice old lady
I helped across the street?"

WARD 5

de CARLO

Largely instrumental

The patient had an embarrassingly situated wen that showed signs of infection. The doctor decided he might be able to probe the wen sac out, so he asked his new and very green aide to get him a curet.

The girl scurried to the instrument case, but paused on sighting the imposing array. Realizing her plight, the doctor gave her directions over his shoulder:

"Third shelf on the right. The instrument with the spoon on the end."

It still wasn't enough. "Big spoon or little spoon?" asked the aide.

In a carefully controlled monotone the physician replied, "The little spoon."

At last the instrument was put to use on the long-suffering patient, and there was much groaning and flinching. When he'd taken all he could, the man burst out with, "My God, Doctor, are you sure she gave you the *little* spoon?"

— *Phyllis G. Malvern,* R.N.

"Only the hands, Gilroy, only the hands."

Negotiable item

The patient whose history I was taking told me she was single. So when I came to the space listing number of children, I automatically put down "None."

"But, Doctor," she said, "I have a 13-year-old daughter."

I reminded her that she'd told me she was an old maid. "I am," she answered. "But I'm not a stubborn old maid!"

— *William H. Miller*, M.D.

Pharmaceutically yours

While examining a Texan who was visiting in my state, I noticed he had a scar on his scalp and questioned him about it. "I got it from being drugged," he told me.

Not seeing the connection, I asked him to elaborate.

"Well," he said, "I was working on a ranch. My horse bolted. My foot got caught in the stirrup. And I was drugged."

— *William L. Sands,* M.D.

· **"Henry and I used to do that before his laminectomy."**

"In the old days, for $75, a doctor would <u>fill</u> a baby carriage!"

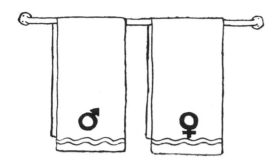

"Didn't you even get his license number?"

Double take

While an interne, I served concurrently in several of my hospital's outpatient specialty clinics. One morning in the medical clinic, I attended a middle-aged female neurotic whose only genuine complaint seemed to be a ringing in the ears.

I assured her there was no organic trouble; but, to allay her fears, I referred her to the otology clinic. There, I told her, she'd have the attention of one of our ear specialists, much better trained in the field than I.

Imagine my consternation when, that afternoon in otology, the specialist who received her turned out to be me.

— *Peter Fisher,* M.D.

"Gerald and I discussed it thoroughly and agreed that
artificial insemination was the best course. . . ."

No sale

While having lunch one day, after my return from service in World
War II, I recognized the man next to me at the counter as Fred Morgan,
a businessman I hadn't seen in years. He was kind enough to compliment me on my service record and to ask how I was getting along.
I took pains to point out that I now specialized in infants and children
and to let him know where my office was located. I intimated that I
was happy to see patients at any time.

Following my verbal onslaught I handed him one of my professional
cards and asked, as an afterthought, what *he* was doing.

"Pediatrics," he answered dryly.

Through a haze of embarrassment I suddenly remembered that he
was not Fred Morgan at all but a local physician I had met once before the war.

— *John McCollough,* M.D.

"... and stop wheeling these twins through the alcoholic ward!"

"You mean I'm well enough to go back to <u>work</u>?"

Saint Vitus

A patient I treated in my office just before Christmas said, "I can't pay you now, Doctor. I'm a circus acrobat, and I've been broke since the circus went into winter quarters."

"In that case," I said, "let's just call it a Christmas present."

"Gee, thanks!" he replied. "But then I've got a present for *you*."

With that he went into his tumbling act right in my reception room. The patients waiting there were fascinated.

Finally, he panted, "Are we even, Doctor?"

When I assured him we were, he bowed to everyone and departed with a booming "Merry Christmas to all!"

— *William Gibson,* M.D.

"Well, daddio, I made the scene after only six months. And was that cord a drag!"

"But, Doctor! Aren't you supposed to <u>reason</u> with them?"

Operation zero

After I'd placed packs in the sinus patient's nose, I asked him to wait outside while I saw some other patients. Later, I went to call him in. But the waiting room was empty. Puzzled, I donned my hat and coat and started home.

Only then did I spot my lost patient, shivering under a street light.

"What's the idea?" I asked him.

"You told me to wait outside," he answered glumly.

— *J. L. Kubrick*, M.D.

Enough for a lifetime

A fortyish matron, mother of two teen-agers, came to me for an examination. She told me she'd missed a couple of periods and was "just wondering . . ." My examination showed that she was unquestionably pregnant.

Noting her expression of dismay, I tried to reassure her. She was in excellent physical condition, I said, and should have no difficulty despite her years.

"Oh, it isn't that, Doctor," she wailed. "I'm not worried about having a baby. I just don't think I can stand 12 more years of P.T.A.!"
— *John Alexander*, M.D.

"You sure put one over on us, Mr. Johnson. We thought we had you covered . . . ha-ha . . . for <u>every</u> type of accident!"

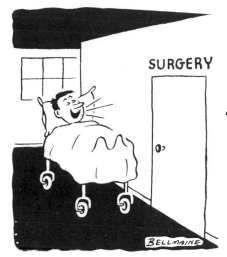

SURGERY

"Su-weet Ad-o-line!"

Deaf ear

A colleague of mine was examining a small boy who'd been brought to the clinic by his mother, a very talkative woman. During the examination my friend noticed that the youngster wasn't paying much heed to his questions. "Do you have trouble hearing?" the doctor asked.

"No," the boy answered. "I have trouble listening."

— *Robert Simpson*, M.D.

"Jim wanted a boy. I just wanted breakfast in bed."

"That cute interne asked me to the movies tonight, but I'm broke."

"There's a talent scout from Mayo's up there!"

Sickroom, shaggy style

In the course of making a house call, I was greeted in the yard by a big, nondescript collie. He followed me to the door and, when the patient's wife opened it, pushed in ahead of me.

No sooner had we entered the sickroom than the dog jumped up on the bed and began licking the patient's face. This show of affection was all right, except that I had to examine the man, and the dog kept getting in the way. I wanted to ask the patient to get his blasted pet off the bed. But I hesitated to offend such an indulgent dog lover.

After I'd completed the visit and was halfway down the front walk, I heard a sharp rapping on the window. It was the patient's wife. "Doctor," she shouted, "you forgot your dog!"

— *John C. Souders Jr.*, M.D.

"AH-H-H-H!"

"Of course not, silly! I'm waiting for Dr. Phelps, my father."

Perfect fit

A young lady came into our surgical appliance store with a prescription for a suspensory for her husband. I asked her what size—small, medium or large. Her brows knit in reflection.

"I'm not certain," she said at last, "but I do know that he wears a size 15½ collar."

— *E. A. Wallick*

Electrotherapy

Many years ago, I had a patient who was a streetcar motorman. One day, at the end of the line, he stepped off his empty car to answer nature's call.

As he did so, he noticed a small fire smoldering in the insulation around the transformer beneath the car; so he did the obvious thing in an attempt to extinguish it. Reaction was immediate. He got a shocking reminder that saline solutions are first-rate conductors of electricity. — *Gordon Smith,* M.D.

"Remember, Mr. Digby, your Foley is still indwelling."

"Why yes, Doctor, we've had a taste of civilized medicine."

Blanket excuse

I was doing a home delivery in a rural area. Three times before, the mother had borne girls. This time the parents and the whispering gallery of neighbors were plainly hoping for a male heir. But once again it was a girl.

I prepared to wrap the baby in a brand-new receiving blanket from Sears, Roebuck. As I did so, a small printed slip fell to the floor. It read: "This is not exactly what you ordered, but we have ventured to substitute the nearest thing in stock, hoping thereby not to delay your order."

— *Hilton A. Wick*, M.D.

No strain

A department store salesgirl came to my office for treatment of a second-degree burn on her leg. After I had taken care of it, I said, "Mary, I want you to stay off that leg for a while."

"That'll be easy, Doctor," she answered in all innocence. "I'm getting married Saturday, and I'll be off my feet for a whole week."
— *Charles Bailey,* M.D.

"One thing more, Doctor: What time in the morning should we wake him?"

Hole in one

It was an ideal day for golf. So I determined to spend the whole afternoon at it. I'd had a hectic morning, but at last I seemed to be in the clear. I strode happily into the reception room for a last look around before taking off.

Immediately my spirits went into mourning. Inexplicably, somehow, the room had become jammed with people—of all sizes, shapes and sexes.

Gloomily, I asked, "Who's first?" Whereupon the oldest occupant followed me into the consultation room.

There I discovered that the poor fellow had more aches than a two-platoon football team. I had to spend a full hour with him. Meanwhile, there was that line-up of people still waiting for me.

Dejectedly, I escorted the old man back to the waiting room. But then, as I watched, my eyes popping, the entire assemblage arose; and each person respectfully fell into line behind the white-haired patriarch as he made his departure.

While driving to the golf club, I reflected happily on the social value of family solidarity.

— *Theo Bold,* M.D.

"It says that under compulsory sickness insurance we won't have to pay no doctor bills. . . . Hell, we don't pay none <u>now</u>!"

"My eyes, ears, nose and throat hurt!"

FRANK RIDGEWAY

'O' marks the spot

Once, while shorthanded in my office, I gave hip injections without benefit of draping. Only one patient demurred. She was a little spinster in her sixties, who, rather than lift her skirt, asked me to give the injection in her arm. I did so.

By the time of her next visit, I had forgotten the incident completely, so I again asked her to get ready for a hip injection. Dutifully she raised her skirt, revealing to my wonder-struck eyes a round opening, two inches across, neatly buttonholed in her knitted pants.

— *Charles Miller,* M.D.

"Dr. Blimpton, <u>please</u> . . . let's not talk shop."

"But, Doctor, you **told** me to cut the I.V."

Shot in the head

The patient, whom I'd never seen before, arrived at my office pale and breathless. Collapsing into a chair, she managed to open her handbag. "Quick! Here's the ampule!" she gasped.

It was aminophylline, and I injected it pronto. She got up and began to thank me. In mid-sentence she dropped to the floor, out cold. I hoisted her back into the chair, now panicky myself. I'd opened the office only three days before. Was one of my first patients to die there?

Luckily, in a few minutes she was conscious again. With gushing gratitude, she pressed five crisp dollar bills into my hand. "They told me I'm allergic to it," she said, "and I keel over every time I take it. But I feel *so* much better afterwards."

— *Charles Peterson*, M.D.

"Here, here, Pemberton. Some other time we'll get the tonsils!"

"Mrs. Hendrick's baby is crying and won't go to sleep. What should she do?"

"I'm sorry, Mr. Herbert, but visiting hours are over."

Distal view

The professor of surgery at a large medical center had just completed a brilliant, hour-long operation. As usual, he'd had the copious aid of the house staff, including a new interne who, back among the third tier of assistants, had been permitted to hold the distal end of a long retractor.

"Well, my lad," the surgeon asked him, as the team rested in the dressing room, "did you learn anything this morning?"

"Yes, sir," the interne answered. "I can now state categorically that the assistant resident has dandruff."

— *Marvin L. Thompson,* M.D.

1.

2.

3.

4.

LÁSZLO

"Come, come, Mr. Fidd! Early ambulation is a vital part of your post-op care."

Gratitude compounded

He was the town ne'er-do-well. I'd delivered his wife of four daughters in as many years without once being paid. When he got me out of bed at 2 o'clock one winter night as the mercury hovered near zero, I was all set to give him a piece of my mind. But he spiked my guns by saying:

"My wife's having another baby, Doctor. The pains are coming about five minutes apart. She told me to go to another doctor so's not to bother you again; but I didn't want to hurt your feelings. After all, *you're* our family doctor!"

— *John Evans*, M.D.

"How should I know his name?
He can't talk yet."

"N.P.O. Monday, liquids Tuesday, solids Wednesday, and today—The Wall Street Journal!"

"Dad, can I have the ambulance tonight?"

Catalyst

A friend who was about to take a high-strung Persian cat with him on an airline flight asked me how to keep him quiet. Being a cocksure interne, I told him to bring the cat around just before he left and I'd fix everything. He did so, and I injected the animal with close to a grain of morphine. A week later came this letter:

"I don't know how to thank you for your help with Percival. As it was, I could scarcely manage him. He scratched a woman's face and knocked the hat off an indignant old man. I shudder to think what he would have been like if you *hadn't* given him the sedative."

It was then I recalled something about cats and morphine being an explosive mixture. I went straight to the books, and there it was: "On cats, opiates act as violent central nervous system stimulators."
— *William MacDonald,* M.D.

"I remarried three years ago."

WM. THOMSON

Thin-skinned

The young Portuguese housewife was suffering from a circumscribed neurodermatitis of the neck. When I told her it was of emotional origin and that she must be unhappy about something, her eyes filled with tears.

"Could be it's my husband, Doctor," she said, brokenly. "He's very mean man. All the time he hit me, all the time he scream at me. 'Get lost, you bastid. Drop dead, you bastid,' he say."

She wept softly for some moments, then looked up. "I don't know, though," she said, pensively. "Could be I'm too sensitive."

— *James Robertson*, M.D.

"To put it nontechnically, Mr. Lonk, yours is a simple case of too much birds and bees."

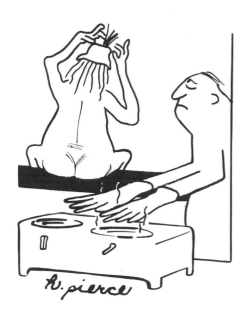

"It isn't <u>anything</u> spelled backwards. It's Latin."

Short-winded

Before starting a post-mortem, we decided that a chest X-ray was called for. The cadaver was wheeled into the X-ray department and propped up under the technician's supervision.

She was about to make the exposure when, from force of habit, she stuck her head out from behind the control panel and called, "All right now, take a deep breath and hold it!"

— *Charles Harris*, M.D.

"Well, all I can say is it hasn't happened in 1,963 years!"

Breadwinner

The farmer's wife had just given birth to a strapping youngster. Anxiously, the father asked me about the sex of the newborn. I told him he had just added a fine little girl to his growing brood.

"Aw, shucks," he complained, "what I need is a plowhand."

At this point my wife, who had assisted at the delivery, spoke up in defense of the fair sex: "Well, what's wrong with a good hoer?" The silence was deafening.

— *W. A. Mecom,* M.D.

"Don't be so ornery, Paw! Go ahead and breathe a coupla times fer 'im."

Factory-rebuilt

Quite a few years ago a native from deep in the interior was brought to our Persian Gulf hospital. His leg had been crushed under a huge rock. Once over the initial shock, he exhibited unusual good spirits. This was his first contact with white men and civilization. Even as simple a thing as turning on an electric light seemed a first-class miracle to him.

A few days after performing the necessary amputation, the doctor asked him, via an interpreter, how he felt. "Just fine," the patient answered. "The leg doesn't hurt a bit since you took it off. When will it be well enough to put back on?"

— *William Duncan*, M.D.

"I guess he's gonna stay. He's got his hat off."

"Wow! Er . . . I mean hmmm!"

"Mr. Fonting called. That gizmo on his watchamacallit is bothering him again."

—GHWHITE—

"Well, the first time I noticed this little hickey on my elbow was last Tuesday—no, Wednesday—at Mabel Gordon's bridge party. I remember distinctly, because I said to Eloise Faraday—she was Eloise Mitchell before she married Abner Faraday . . ."

The lady and the tiger

As a young woman interne, I thought histories and physicals pretty dull stuff until I drew a certain young man as a patient. When I entered his hospital room, there he was, devastatingly handsome in dark blue silk pajamas and white ascot. On the verge of swooning, I nevertheless maintained my composure until it came time to examine his chest.

Then I found that both the stethoscope and I were too short to reach the middle of the bed. So in my best professional manner I said, "Will you please move over?"

"Why sure," he grinned and, with that, moved to the *other* side of the bed, invitingly making room for me.

— *Mary Johnson*, M.D.

"E, m, Ǝ, E, ɯ, ɯ, Ǝ."

Undercover man

An attending surgeon at our hospital had never been known to admit a mistake. One day, while doing a laparotomy for an intestinal obstruction, he inadvertently nicked the bladder. The mishap was repaired in a matter of seconds, and the patient made a complete recovery. When dictating his report on the bowel surgery, the doctor added this note: "Exploration of the bladder failed to reveal the presence of stones."

— *Philip Smith,* M.D.

Double or nothing

One of my hospitalized patients was complaining loudly that he hadn't received an enema I'd ordered several days before. The nurses and the resident were quick to assure me that the patient was mistaken. The nurse even produced some notes stating that the enema had been given the day before with good results.

At this point, the patient in the next bed spoke up: "Well, yesterday they gave *me* two of them!"

— *Richard Martin*, M.D.

"Spare a buck for a tranquilizer, buddy?"

"Who was it who said you can't eat your cake and have 'it,' too?"

"Isn't he cute!"

"I can't stand these hideous slipcovers any longer. Didn't you say something about needing new drapes at the office?"

Frozen asset

A patient I hadn't seen for a decade or so came to my office. She said she feared her husband had embarked on an extramarital adventure. Since she'd had no normal relations with him for nine years, she didn't blame him; but she was nonetheless upset.

Our conversation revealed that nine years earlier she'd had some pelvic surgery. After it, her surgeon had told her to abstain from physical contact with her husband. Of course he meant until healing was complete. But she misunderstood. Now, incredulous but happy, she left my office, resolved to make up for lost time.

— *William Martin*, M.D.

"How are you, Bill?—rhetorically, that is."

Hour of truth

In broken English, the excited voice on the phone asked for the doctor. Since he was busy with a patient, I asked if I, his aide, could take a message. The caller stammered, "Tell doctor, my wife she is going to get well."

"That's fine," I said. "The doctor will be glad to hear it. I'll tell him as soon as he's free."

"No, no!" cried the voice. "Tell doctor to come quick. My wife, she is going to have baby!"

And so she did, recovering promptly from her nine months' illness.
— *Millie Travers*

"Wait . . . wait! The thermometer!"

"Want to floor him? Just tell him to give you a shot of testosterone."

But no happy return

My aide was preparing my bills at the end of the month and came across an account that had been outstanding just one day short of 12 months. Making out a new statement, she added a postscript: "Tomorrow this bill will be a year old."

Two days later, back the statement came. On it the patient had scrawled, "Happy Birthday!"

— *Richard Nelson*, M.D.

"Just read it, Mr. Mafooski; don't translate it."

"I have it on good authority, Peebles, that your blood pressure is down and your ulcer is inactive. Am I to conclude from this that you no longer care about moving up in the firm?"

No grass widow

A surgeon I know likes to putter around his estate on his afternoons off. One day, dressed in his oldest clothes, he was pushing a mower over the lawn, near the road. A car pulled up and a dowager stuck her head out the window. "I say," she called, "what do you get for mowing lawns?"

The surgeon paused, puffed at his pipe, then answered, "Well, the lady here usually lets me sleep with her."

— *John McLeod*, M.D.

"You're the <u>only</u> reason I want to get well!"

Conversation piece

A 5-year-old boy accompanied his mother and his new baby sister to our office. The doctor ushered the mother and infant into his treatment room, and it became my lot, as the receptionist, to entertain the young man. I told him he was lucky to have such an exceptional baby sister. "I wish *I* had a lovely little baby like Linda at *my* house," I burbled.

In a voice that carried to every corner of the crowded reception room, the boy replied, "Then why don't you do what my mommy did —quit running around nights and stay home and get pregnant?"
— *Susan Grinder*

"How does it look to you, Doc—I mean spleenwise?"

"Gosh, I bet you wuz surprised when you heard about it!"

"Is she allowed visitors yet?"

"The bubble gum backfired."

"You kids better stand back. You might catch my broken leg."

Trainman's holiday

A friend of mine, the medical director of a railroad, was baffled by an employe who kept asking for days off, each time on the excuse that his wife had "had a childbirth." The worker's first and second requests were granted without question, although they were only a few weeks apart. But when, a fortnight later, he came in with the same story, the doctor took him to task.

"How is it possible for your wife to have experienced childbirth three times in six weeks?" he asked.

"She's a midwife," the man replied. "Whenever she goes out on a job, I have to stay home and take care of the kids."

— *E. Cros*, M.D.

"You say I charged you for a visit on the 24th, yet I didn't see you that day. . . . You're quite right. That was the day I <u>worried</u> about you."

"No, I'm sorry. The doctor is feeling under par today."

Nocturnal nugget

A young female patient had been delivering a long monologue about her countless ailments. Finally, I was forced to stifle a yawn. "Too much night work," I smiled, by way of excusing myself.

"It is *not!*" she retorted. "I don't live with my husband any more."
— *James Boyd*, M.D.

No deal

I was called out at 3 A.M. to catheterize a patient in severe distress. A week later the man dropped by my office. "Don't you think, Doctor," he said, "that $20 is a bit steep for that visit?"

I promptly made him a proposition. "If you'll get up at 3 A.M. tomorrow, put on your clothes, back your car out of the garage, drive to my home and sit by my bed and talk to me for 45 minutes, I'll call it square."

The patient thought it over for a moment. Then, reaching for his wallet, he said with a grin, "Do you think $20 is *enough?*"
— *William Reed,* M.D.

"He has your eyes."

"Frankly, Whitmore, Acme Research feels that in turning penicillin back to mold, you haven't accomplished a hell of a lot."

"Neck 17½ . . . chest 42 . . . pot 58 . . ."

The Army way

While serving my Army stint, I decided to prepare a paper for my home state medical journal. So I put my enlisted staff to work abstracting chart data, and I assigned a bright young sergeant the job of averaging the long columns of statistics.

Finally he handed me the results: the patients' average age, average hospital stay, average this and average that. On the last sheet, for good measure, he'd included a figure that I suspect mirrored his view of the value of all the others: a carefully computed average of the patients' case history numbers.

— *Samuel B. Thompson*, M.D.

"Well, it's just that I haven't been myself lately—and I'd like to keep it that way."

Last straw

I had just lost a patient with myelogenous leukemia. His family appeared to understand that I had done everything possible to keep him alive. They weren't bitter. Yet, surprisingly, they refused permission for a post-mortem.

I walked along with them as they left the hospital, trying desperately to explain the need. But my appeals were in vain.

Finally, the daughter turned to me and said, "Doctor, I don't want you to think we're ungrateful for all you've done. We'd like to help you out by authorizing a post-mortem. But to tell you the honest truth, we just can't afford it."

— *Charles Long*, M.D.

"Here's one that looks interesting: 'Will Hitler Really Invade Poland?' "

Collection technique

The patient was receiving a post-hemorrhoidectomy treatment consisting of dilatation of the anus. As I inserted a gloved finger, he remarked that his insurance check had arrived and that they'd allowed him $20 less than my bill for surgery.

At that point I must have touched a tender spot, for he yelped with pain, then blurted frantically, "But it's O.K., Doc. It's O.K. I'll pay the difference!"

— *M. Rothenberg,* M.D.

"Aren't you making a hell of a fuss over a wart?"

"Is the doctor in?"

Cantankerously yours

For some years a doctor-friend of mine had been submitting articles to medical journals without much luck. Nearly all had been rejected. Late last fall, however, he crashed through with two acceptances by a national journal of top reputation.

In a warm glow, he sat down and wrote the editors a note of appreciation, including his best wishes for a Merry Christmas and a Happy New Year. In due course the letter was returned—with a rejection slip.

— *Pauline Hall*

"Wilma, you haven't lived till you've had a date with a chiropractor."

One for the books

In World War II, we once asked headquarters to send an EENT specialist to our Army hospital. They sent an eye man. I phoned and said we needed someone skilled in ear, nose and throat work as well. This dialogue followed:

"What's wrong with the man we sent you?"

"Nothing, but he's an eye specialist only."

"You've got medical books there, haven't you?"

"Yes."

"Well, he can read, can't he?"

— *James Adams*, M.D.

"How come your handwriting's suddenly so legible?"

"Certainly carrots will strengthen your eyesight. You never saw a rabbit wearing glasses, did you?"

"That's a refresher?!"

"This is no time to be 'feeling better already.'
We haven't even finished the diagnosis."

"I just received my doctor's bill. Print me up some money."

Two bits for a haircut

Several months after having had a mastoidectomy, one of our hospital's new lab technicians met a medical student in the corridor who said he was on his way to witness a mastectomy. "Oh, I've had one of those," said the young girl. "Bilateral, too."

The medical student stopped short and surveyed her well-developed figure with astonishment. Before he could say anything, the technician asked, "Do you want to see my scars? They used to show quite a lot, but now my hair has grown so long that it covers them."
— *Robert Cunningham*, M.D.

"A **baby**! Are you sure it isn't gas?"

"Please, Mr. Schultz—the doctor's waiting!"

Welcome, stranger!

The young man's trouble was acute laryngitis. He stood hesitantly in the reception room doorway, eying the blonde nurse. "Is the doctor in?" he finally managed, in a hoarse whisper.

He wasn't exactly set at ease when the nurse whispered back, "No —come on in!"

— *A. J. Gloss*, M.D.

Rain check

I was taking a teen-ager to the hospital for her first baby. The young husband, even more tense than she, watched in dismay as his wife was seized with a violent labor pain.

"Honey," he asked anxiously, "are you *sure* you want to go through with this?"

— *R. A. White,* M.D.

"Now this won't hurt . . . <u>did</u> it?"

"There **isn't** any 'rest of it.' "

"Tell 66-66-66 to come in."

"Well, what do you think?"

Heads, you lose

The emergency room interne was an overweening fellow who ranked himself somewhere between Osler and God. One day the police ambulance screeched up to the admitting door, and in shuffled two patrolmen carrying a patient covered with a blanket.

"No need to hurry with this guy," one of them said, as they set down the stretcher. "He's dead."

"And how would *you* know?" asked the interne with withering condescension. "Remind me to tell you sometime how many patients presumed dead by would-be diagnosticians have later been revived by physicians."

He then whipped back the blanket to begin his lifesaving work. What met his eyes was a decapitated body, its head tucked neatly under its arm.

— *Frederick W. Knoch,* M.D.

"The light has changed. May I defer my opinion and suggest you visit my office?"

Ask Dad; he knows

An old friend recently brought in her daughter, aged 6, for an examination. While my nurse was helping the little girl to disrobe, I noticed that the mother was pregnant.

"My, my," I said jokingly. "Looks as though you've been eating too much lately."

The little girl poked her head from behind the curtain, gave me a look of utter scorn and said, "That's what *you* think!"

— *Joseph Levy*, M.D.

"Had these scales checked lately, Doctor? According to this table I should be five inches taller."

"You can't sleep? That's funny; neither can I."

In a word

From the question-and-answer column of Britain's "Medical World":
Q. Can you tell me the precise chemical formula, mode of preparation and pharmaceutical properties of dihydroethylhexamethaline tetrachloride?... *A.* No.

"Yes, I <u>know</u> you took out my husband's appendix a year ago. But this is my <u>second</u> husband."

"Do me a favor, Miss Karp: Stop saying, 'You're the doctor.' "

GET-WELL CARDS

"So how much sympathy d'ya <u>expect</u> for a dime?"

Locum tenens

The doctor's wife, bent on preserving his slumber, snatched the bed-side phone from its cradle halfway through the first ring. The 3 A.M. caller explained that her husband had an earache and asked if the doctor would please come at once. "He's not in," said the physician's faithful frau. But at this point the doctor grunted in his sleep.

"Are you sure the doctor isn't in?" the caller asked suspiciously.

"Quite sure," the doctor's wife said. But once again her mate har-rumphed audibly.

"In that case," the caller inquired, "who's that man in bed with you?"
— *Robert Bailey,* M.D.

"Bite him quick. Show him who's boss."

Waiting to accommodate

On my second day in practice in a small town, I was called to the scene of an accident in which two limousines in a funeral procession had collided. Several of the occupants were badly cut, so I took them back to the office with me.

There, for an hour, I debrided, stitched and bandaged. At last I accompanied my patients to the front door, where, to my horror, I discovered the entire funeral procession. It had been drawn up in front of the office the whole time—while, no doubt, the rest of the town concluded what it was there for.

— *Elizabeth Proctor,* M.D.

"I'm sending Mrs. Williams in out of turn.
She's already prescribed for two other patients, and they've left."

"Mind having a look into this thing, old man? There's something staring at me!"

"Now, don't worry. This won't hurt a bit!"

"Plugged sink."

"Sure, honey. . . . I'll take you down to the office Saturday and give you a few tests."

Spreading the word

When my husband and an associate opened an office, they hired a maid to keep the place tidy. One day my husband happened to meet the maid as he approached the office building. He noticed that her usual trim uniform had been replaced by a garish blue garment.

She stepped in front of him and proudly asked, "Doctor, how do you like my new outfit?" Across her ample shoulders, painstakingly embroidered, were the words, "Smith and Finch, M.D., F.A.C.S., Medicine & Surgery, 205 South 4th Street."

— *Zella C. Finch*

"When they removed the stitches,
she just went to pieces."

"Will you please tell me the condition
of Mr. Leemer in Room 503?"

Slightly fatal

I was helping a young patient fill out an insurance application form.
We finished with the data on his mother, and I asked him about his
father. The latter, he told me, had died quite a few years before.

"What was the cause of his death?" I asked.

"I can't quite remember," he said, puckering his brow, "but I'm sure
it was nothing serious."

— *Arnold O. Wirsig*, M.D.

Prognosis deferred

The doctor hadn't much use for the patient's wife, reputed to have married the old boy strictly for his money. But she hovered dutifully by the sickbed as the M.D. made his examination.

"Is there any hope, Doctor?" she finally asked anxiously.

"That depends," he said, "on what you're hoping for."

— *Robert Olson,* M.D.

"I'm happy to inform you, Miss Botts, that your trial period is over. May I see you to the door?"

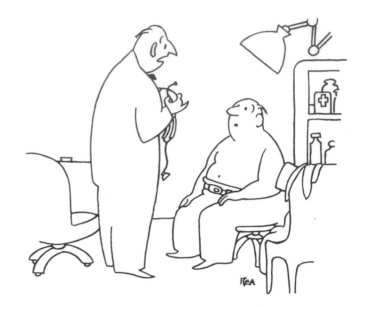

"Someone up there hates your guts."

"This must be one hell of an injection!"

"This time you're wrong. The myelogram was <u>negative</u>."

Flash in the can

One of my ward patients had been given rectal ether to alleviate asthmatic distress. Shortly afterward, he came running back from the men's room in a flurry of excitement.

What he'd intended as a nice, quiet smoke had ended in a flash of ignited fumes when he dropped his still-burning match into the toilet bowl.

Result: one scorched perineum.

— *Robert E. Lee*, M.D.

Pediatrics

Bob Kling

Countdown

An elderly Kansas G.P. once told me about his first OB case: When he arrived on the scene, he found the expectant mother surrounded by four elderly women from the neighborhood, all sitting in rockers, knitting. After examining the pregnant woman, the doctor concluded that the birth would occur in a few hours.

One of the watchers then laid aside her knitting and said, "Doctor, is it time to feather her?"

Not having the faintest idea what she meant, the doctor nevertheless replied, "No, not yet."

After the next examination, the question was repeated, and again the doctor stalled. The old women continued to knit.

Finally, it became evident that the baby was about due. So when asked again whether the prospective mother should be feathered, the doctor said, "Yes, I think it's time."

At that, two of the knitters jumped from their rockers, whipped two goose feathers out of a pillow and thrust them up the nostrils of the patient. She let loose a prodigious sneeze and a newborn infant landed in the lap of the dumfounded doctor.

He knew now what "feathering" meant.

— *Tom Ebbinghouse*, M.D.

1

2

3

TON SMITS

4

Parting shot

When the doctor arrived at the tiny backwoods cabin, he found relatives packed solidly in the sickroom. The aged patient had suffered a stroke and was near the end. Feeling that he had to do something, the physician decided to give the old man an injection. But just as he inserted the needle, the patient gave a loud gasp and died.

The room was silent for a moment. Then a hushed voice from the far corner said, "Lordy, he sure killed him quick!"

— *T. C. McEntee*

". . . printed by Ajax Chart Company, Hartford, Connecticut."

"I don't care whether it's bigger than both of us or not; it's still against the rules!"

"I've just become a brother!"

Clocktomania

I had an inexpensive but charming little clock on my waiting room mantel. One day it disappeared. So I philosophically replaced it with a similar one. Next week a woman came in for her weekly visit, accompanied by her small son.

"Oh, look, Mommy!" he shrilled in front of me, my aide and the other patients. "There's another clock just like the one you got here last week!"

— *James Alexander*, M.D.

"I just washed him, and I can't do a thing with him!"

Turnabout tale

Respect for our family physician's skill as a psychologist was instilled in me by an incident that occurred in my childhood. When my younger brother was born, the doctor noted my jealous reaction. Thinking quickly, he said, "Oh, I've made a mistake. I've left this boy at the wrong house. He belongs to the Browns down the street."

At once my jealousy was converted to fear—fear that I would lose my new playmate. I begged the doctor not to take the baby away. "Well, I'll see what I can do," he replied.

I was the happiest kid in the block when he dropped by next day to say I could keep my brother after all.
— *Maymie R. Krythe*

"You and your bedside manner!"

"We want you to give Blathers a checkup. He's been working under pressure lately."

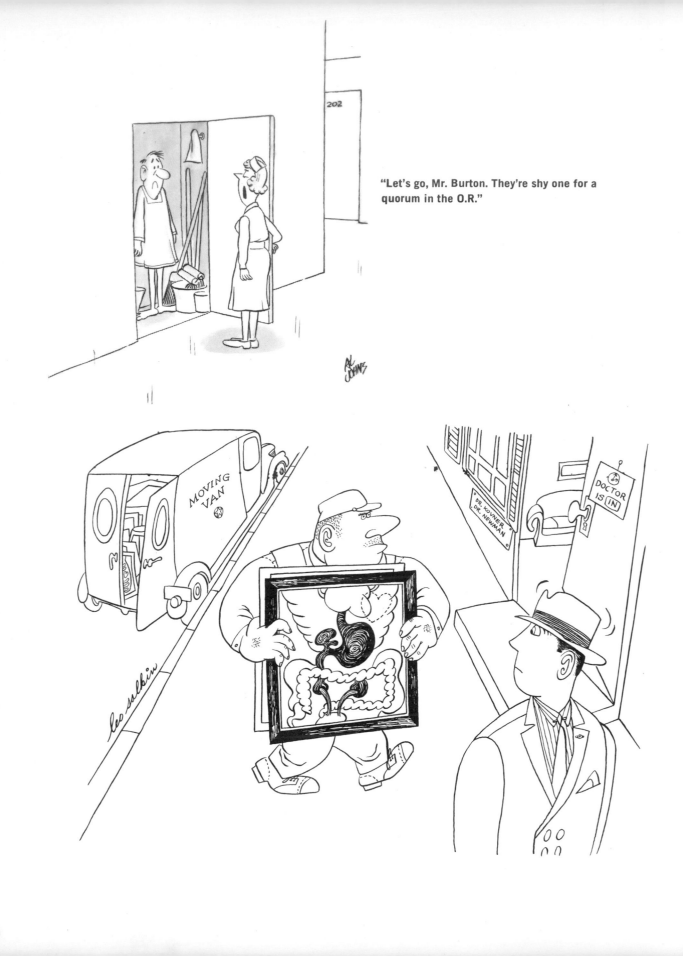

"Let's go, Mr. Burton. They're shy one for a quorum in the O.R."

"... and this little piggy tells us you have a Babinski."

Soft-boiled

I'd had great difficulty getting to the remote farmhouse in time to deliver a husky boy. Yet for a full year thereafter, the father ignored my bill for $20. When I finally went to see him about it, he told me:

"Doc, I figger I don't owe you nothin'. That there shot you give the old woman give the baby a soft spot on top his head. I been takin' him to a chiropractor since he was 4 months old, and the chiropractor says he won't be able to git that soft spot hardened up till the kid is at least 18 months old."

— *Robert Foster*, M.D.

"I must be getting old. My wife has stopped
hiring and firing my office girls."

"Will you cough up a quarter? Or do I have to
throw a grand mal with tonic and clonic components?"

Second courtship

Soon after the delivery, the young mother was taken to her room,
where her husband and her mother-in-law were permitted to visit her.
The patient was still groggy, so the husband was content just to hold
her hand.

A while later the young mother, unaware of the presence of her
mother-in-law, said: "Honey, after this we'll have to be real careful
—just like before we were married."

— *James A. Johnson*, M.D.

Plenty of cents

My 8-year-old daughter answered the doorbell. No, her daddy wasn't in, she informed the caller. "He's at the hospital, doing an appendectomy."

"My," said the caller, "that's a big word for a little girl. Do you know what it means?"

"Sure I do," she answered promptly. "It means $150."
— *John Simmons*, M.D.

"Hello, Raymond. It worked!"

"Well, it's about time! I was going to start without you!"

"Hey! That's Brooks Brothers you're cutting up!"

"What's good for appendicitis?"

Busy body

The young woman who entered the pediatric clinic with a small baby complained that the child was taking his breast feeding poorly. Our professor considered the case of sufficient interest to call in the entire section.

He asked the young woman to undress so that each of us—eight in all—could palpate her breasts, noting how underdeveloped and nodular they were. After we'd finished, he explained to her the course she must follow to improve lactation.

Only then did she volunteer the information that the child was not hers but her sister's.

— *Harry Hoffman,* M.D.

"The doctor isn't in. . . . Would you care to leave your name?"

Dark circles

Early one spring, a young woman came to my office complaining of frequent nausea. I knew little about her; but since she had a sister of questionable reputation, I at once suspected her trouble. It seemed even more probable when I examined her and saw her darkened areolae. I remarked that they were, in fact, as dark as a pregnant woman's.

She sighed—then nodded. "I guess I *am* pregnant, Doctor."

"In that case," I said, "my advice to you is to marry the boy."

Her eyes narrowed. "I did," she replied coldly, "last June."

— *F. Clyde Bedsaul*, M.D.

"We hate to leave so soon, but Fred is all
tuckered out. He handled 11 surgery cases today!"

"Why don't you ever give _me_ some of those happy pills?"

"It's gonna be tough on the kids. I'll have to <u>kick</u> 'em for a while."

"I'd like to see their faces at the drugstore
when they get <u>this</u> one!"

Clipped

I was taking a history of a male patient prior to gastrointestinal X-rays. When I asked if he'd ever had any operations, he took a quick look at my secretary sitting nearby, then replied sotto voce, "Yes— when I was 8 days old."

— *William Ferguson,* M.D.

"Twenty-five bucks an hour? . . . I m̲ust be nuts!"

"Now, I want you to be quite frank with me."

Trunk line

My office was crowded with patients. The phone had been ringing all day. By late afternoon I felt mentally and physically exhausted. Then, right in the middle of a difficult chest examination, the phone rang again. I hurried to it and was kept there 10 minutes before I could hang up and get back to the examining room.

Where was I? Oh, yes—chest examination. The nurse handed me my stethoscope. Placing it on the woman's chest, I said wearily, "Hello?"
— *H. W. Garton*, M.D.

"Maybe he just isn't feeling well."

"I'm already pushing 50. That's enough
exercise for anyone!"

"Of course, technically, this is a house call."

"I just had lunch!"

"Why not a tourniquet? He's got a nosebleed, hasn't he?"

"Talk into the thing, Paw. The doc's probably hard o' hearin'."

Minor oversight

A mother rushed into the waiting room of my pediatric office and plopped down in a chair with a "Whew!" of relief. After she got her breath back, she settled back to await her turn on the appointment schedule.

Then, suddenly, without warning she burst into a fit of wild laughter. When my receptionist hurried over to ask what was wrong, she replied: "My God! I left the *baby* home!"

— *Warren R. Tepper*, M.D.

"Couldn't you just undress me mentally, the way other men do?"

"Bifocals!"

"Is Mom going to lay an egg?"

Arch sufferer

A woman with a possible foot fracture was sent to me for X-ray examination. When I told her my bill would be $7.50, she blew up.

"That's outrageous," she complained. "Why, my shoe store has been taking X-rays of my feet for years without *any* charge!"

— *Robert Green*, M.D.

Rare vintage

One of our clinic patients had been told to bring in a urine specimen. She arrived without it, then recalled she'd left it in her car. She went out for it, but returned empty-handed to report that it had apparently been stolen.

How come? She explained that she had used a bottle bearing the label "Old Grand-Dad."
— *Elizabeth McDonagh*

"Where did you say the love bug bit you?"

"Can I leave my glasses on?"

"How do you expect to get well if you don't even look at your get-well cards?"

"After all, Doctor, who's to decide what's normal and what isn't?"

Cold feet

The old man had suffered a foot injury, but it was nothing compared with the injury to my nostrils when I removed his shoes. With all the delicacy I could muster, I asked him if he ever took time out to wash his feet.

"No," he said, "I never put 'em in water. The doctor tole me not to."

Baffled, I asked, "How did that happen?"

"Well, you see, I'd froze my feet, and my folks was just going to put 'em in some warm water; but the doctor said, real emphatic, 'Don't ever do that to feet like that.' "

"How long ago was that?"

"Oh, that was when I was a boy."

Fifty years late, I prescribed warm water—and soap.

— *M. B. Durfee*, M.D.

"We couldn't get 3 out of 4 doctors to endorse it. In fact, we couldn't get 3 out of 745 doctors to endorse it."

Situation in hand

Six of us, all mature M.D.s, were playing golf together before an evening medical meeting. We were being overtaken by two younger golfers. Suddenly one of our group was hit in the head by an oncoming ball. The pain was intense, and all five of us gathered around our injured colleague solicitously.

Just then the young man who'd hit the drive pushed his way through the group, shouting "Gangway! I'm a medical student. Let me through so I can examine this man!"

— *Charles Henderson*, M.D.

"Now I know just what you doctors go through to learn your profession. I've just completed two weeks of my first-aid course."

"He says he doesn't have to."

"What did you expect? Slave girls in gauze pantaloons?"

Neat trick

My husband, a salesman, told me his boss had just had a gallbladder operation. He suggested I write him a note. When I did so, I said I could appreciate what he was going through because I had recently had the same operation.

My husband learned later that what his boss had been operated on for was not gallbladder trouble at all but an enlarged prostate!
— *Mary O'Brien,* R.N.

"Now that that's over, let's grab the Manual and get out of here."

"When you're going crazy, he helps you."

"The hypertonus has gone out of our marriage."

Saturation point

Before the days of sulfa drugs, a backwoods father brought his baby to me for an otitis media. I directed him to run a quart of hot water into the baby's ear every two hours. The father looked at me incredulously and said, "Doctor, you reckon his head gonna hold all that water?" — *H. L. Baptist*, M.D.

"Promise her anything, but give her a belt in the kisser!"

Till the cows come home

While my husband was on Army duty, I stored all his equipment and furniture in his consultation room. Our three small children used the waiting room as a playroom.

On entering the waiting room one afternoon, I found a little old man wedged into a small rocking chair. Toys, books and games were everywhere. All the furniture was child-sized. The only magazine he'd been able to find was a comic book.

When I asked if I could help him, he smiled with total unconcern and said, "Oh, no, thank you. I'm just waiting for the doctor."

— *Vee Glosser*

"The doc asked Gran'pappy if he had to git up in the night to pass water. . . . You figger he knows an easier way?"

"Ethel, I love you, Ethel! You <u>are</u> Ethel, aren't you?"

"Frankly, Mrs. Banshuk, since it's only a dime, it would be a losing proposition."

"You'd better get her south for the winter—to Alaska."

Prenatal influence

I was just establishing a small-town practice when I delivered a young matron of a child with six digits on each hand and foot. Speculation about the phenomenon was soon rife among the townspeople, with explanations ranging from prenatal marking to prenatal diet.

Perhaps the pattest explanation of all was vouchsafed by a mother who announced positively, "That's what comes of having a young, inexperienced doctor!"

— *Charles R. Harris*, M.D.

"But how do we <u>know</u> you'll use it to correct your electrolyte imbalance?"

Matter of relativity

My patient was waiting for a man named Frank to take him home
from the hospital. "Is Frank a relative?" I asked.

"Not any more," replied the patient.

That stumped me—until he explained: "Frank used to be my brother-
in-law, but my wife ain't alive no more."

— *William Donald,* M.D.

Partners in pleasure

I was dismissing a patient I'd just declared cured of gonorrhea. "Well, Sam," I quipped, "better luck next time." Beaming with pleasure, Sam replied, "Good luck to *you*, too, Doctor!"
— *James Nolan*, M.D.

"As the consultant suggested by me, you'll agree with my findings, I'm sure."

"Come on! All the way out!"

"All right, then, have it your way!"

"Green thumb you've got there!"

Rigorous mortification

One midnight, during my interneship, a ward nurse called me to say that a patient had just died. Pending my examination of the deceased, I sat down at the chart desk to complete his papers. Soon the ward door opened and out came a stretcher, headed for the elevator.

"Don't take that body down yet," I barked at the orderly, "I haven't pronounced it dead."

At that, the "body" snapped bolt upright and two terror-filled eyes transfixed me.

An emergency appendectomy, it turned out.

— *S. P. Ivins,* M.D.

"Instead of the usual lub-dub, I'm getting a crazy fizz-wiffle!"

Slice of life

The father of an OB resident I know was convalescing from an illness and needed help in running his small butcher shop. So his son used to go over after he left the maternity ward, don a straw hat and help out slicing up chops and steaks.

Business was disrupted one day when a woman customer suddenly swooned. Seems she recognized the blood-spattered butcher as the same man who, a few weeks before, had delivered her baby.

— *G. R. Mitchell*, M.D.

"By the way, Feebish, I wouldn't start any continued stories if I were you . . ."

"I think it means he's not very good in other specialties; so the A.M.A. or somebody limits him to acne and stuff."

"You've taken your boards, I assume."

"You're the greatest, Pop."

Clairvoyant

A pediatrician-friend of mine had been getting more than his share of telephone queries for free advice. The last straw was a mother who called him to report that 4-year-old Johnny's skin was broken out.

"What do you suppose it is, Doctor?" she asked.

"I don't know," he snapped. "Hold him up so I can get a better look."
— *Donald Morrison*, M.D.

"Why, Agnes!" "Why, Edith!"

"Yes, dear, it's a very practical idea. But do you think I'm the type to introduce it?"

"Well, what has Mary Baker Eddy got to say about this?"

The marauder

It was midnight. Not a sound came from the pediatric ward. I tip-toed from bed to bed to be sure each youngster was resting comfortably before I turned in. Next to the last bed, I noticed an open box of candy. Silently, I stepped over and took a piece.

The following day during visiting hours, I entered the ward again. Suddenly a child's voice rang through the room—and every eye focused on me. "There he is, Mommy!" cried the voice indignantly. "That's the doctor who stole my candy!"

— *W. F. McDonald,* M.D.

"Do you play hockey?"

"No . . . bridge."

"Quick, somebody . . . another bottle!"

"I get working spells."

"I was just about to say 'I do' . . . when ole fickle fate stepped in."

"She says the tumor has blue eyes."

"What an even disposition—always mad."

Fish story

The old man had been seeing me for some time, and I was convinced
his trouble was psychosomatic. When I urged him to unburden himself, he confessed that he worried constantly about his wife. "I'm
always scared she may leave me for some other man," he said.

"So what?" I replied cheerfully. "There are plenty of other fish in
the sea."

"Maybe so," he said gloomily, "but my bait ain't what it used to be."
— *James Lyons*, M.D.

"Here . . . hold it while I tie the cord."

Payoff

As a hospital pathologist, I perform some of my post-mortems in funeral homes. One day I had to wait more than half an hour for a taxi to take me to the local undertaker's. By the time the cab showed up, I was determined to teach the driver a lesson.

"I hope you realize," I said ominously, "that I had to wait so long for you that my patient died in the meantime. Now you may as well take me over to the funeral home."

The shock reflected in the driver's face prophesied some sleepless nights ahead.

— *J. H. Ahronhelm*, M.D.

"If I hear the word 'prostate' mentioned once more here—I'll resign!"

"We take from Dr. Martin; who supplies you?"

"An' after we collect the bill the guy's a patient again, see?"

"Can you explain it to me in something simpler than 'layman's terms'?"

"Hurry up with that cough medicine, Pop. We wanna play spin the bottle."

A la carte

A lunch counter near my office is a favorite spot among physicians in the neighborhood. One day a group of us noticed that Willie, the counterman, was doing a lot of fidgeting. Between times he would scratch his rear end on the corner of the counter.

Several of us tried on-the-spot diagnoses, coming up with as many answers as there were M.D.s present. Finally I asked, "Willie, have you got hemorrhoids?"

Pointing to the bill of fare above the counter, he answered, "Just what's on the menu, Doc."

— *James King*, M.D.

"I don't know what it's called in Latin, but it's a hell of a nasty cramp."

Tight squeeze

The patient complained of pain in her side caused by kidney stones. A faith healer had been treating her; but when the pain became extreme, he'd referred her to our clinic.

I asked what treatment the faith healer had given her to afford even temporary relief. Her answer was that he'd massaged several stones out through her navel.

— *James Elliott*, M.D.

"Dig that crazy beat!"

"If you're lookin' for them little jars, I threw 'em away. The stuff in 'em was all moldy."

Hippocratic huddle

Slipping out one evening for a bridge game with the boys, the young surgeon tossed his wife the most high-sounding excuse he could think of: "Very important case," he said solemnly. "There are three doctors there already."
— *Gerald M. Banker*

"You'll live longer if you give up drinking, smoking and women. At least it'll seem longer."

"Mrs. McGump can come any time after office hours that's convenient for you."

"Well, last night the pain started here . . ."

Mr. Fixit

The young married woman was draped and ready for examination. When I took my seat at the foot of the examining table, I discovered that my sponge forceps were slightly loose. As I tried to adjust the instrument, my nurse said, "Give it a rap with a hammer."

The patient twitched convulsively, raised her head and let out an anguished "Doctor, you *wouldn't!*"

— *Cyrus Leslie Walton*, M.D.

"Your duties will be comparatively simple, Miss Boyce: Greet the patients, answer the telephone, record names and addresses of new patients, take down preliminary case histories, make appointments, schedule surgery, replace supplies and linens, tidy up, prepare patients for examinations, lay out instruments, open the mail . . ."

In all things reciprocity

On taking my leave of a small hospital where I'd been a patient for several weeks, I rewarded my orderly with a sizable tip and praised him for his good work.

Eager to express his gratitude, he came up with the highest compliment he could think of: "We're going to miss you, sir. You sure take a swell enema."

— *John F. Kelly*, M.D.

This way out

My reception room was jammed. I was working as fast as I could, but some patients were growing restless. Finally an old man hoisted himself from his chair, picked up his hat and started for the door.

"Guess I may as well go on home," he announced, "and let death come naturally."

— *William H. Brown*, M.D.

**"If you don't eat, you won't grow up strong and be
a doctor and not have time for breakfast."**

"Look who's got athlete's foot."

"My current period of depression started when I got your bill for the last one."

"Your new drug looks promising all right, Dibbs; but who'll you try it out on?"

What's not going on here?

A male nurse in a mental hospital spotted a patient with his ear to the wall, listening intently. The patient held up a warning finger, then beckoned the nurse to come over quietly. "You listen here," he whispered.

The nurse put his ear to the wall, then turned to the patient and said, "I can't hear anything."

"No," said the patient knowingly, "and it's been like that all day."
— *Robert Palmer*, M.D.

"Which do you like best, granite or marble?"

"Not the Dr. Wassermann?"

Lip reader

I'd just finished examining and treating an elderly, deaf woman in her home. As I got ready to leave, she asked loudly, "How much, Doctor?"

When I said, "Four dollars," she bellowed, "Eh? How much?"

At that point I remembered I'd injected penicillin, so I corrected my fee and replied, "Six dollars."

Came the prompt response: "I heard you the first time."
— *John W. Williams,* M.D.

Diagnostic aid

A colleague of mine was examining a patient he'd known for a long time. She had a minor but obscure ailment. After giving her a thorough physical, the doctor shook his head and said jokingly:

"Well, I don't know for sure what you have. But if you like, I'll give you this medicine. It will produce a fit—and I'm sure hell on fits!"
— *George Mitchell*, M.D.

"You mean Mitch will have to sing along without him?"

"You don't take 'em; you count 'em!"

S.R.O.

After I'd entered the new patient's name in the appointment book, I asked him to be seated while awaiting his turn with the doctor. To my surprise, he refused and started to pace the corridor. Finally I said, "Sir, if you'll have a chair, you'll be more comfortable and the doctor will see you just as soon."

His answer was a snort: "Young lady, if I could sit down, I wouldn't *have* to see the doctor!"

— *Mildred Barr*

"So long, lover boy!"

"I beg your pardon: My husband is terribly seasick, and I remembered your telling me that your husband is a doctor . . ."

"But, Doctor, Hopkins has made five tries and it always comes out a Tom and Jerry!"

"I switched to Gibsons when Engelbarth published his work on olives and cirrhosis."

Wrong number

A dermatologist I know had just finished examining and prescribing for a new patient, a man whose frugality was legend. Voluble in his thanks, the patient produced his wallet, shucked off the rubber band and laboriously counted out three one-dollar bills.

"My fee is *10* dollars," the physician informed him.

"Oh, excuse me, Doctor," said the patient. "My friend told me it was five."

— *James A. Brussel*, M.D.

Self-contained

I'm a doctor's aide. One day while seated at the reception desk, engrossed in some complicated insurance forms, I caught a glimpse of a youth entering the office. In a moment, he was standing before me, saying, "The doctor wants a urine specimen. Where do I put it?"

Without looking up a second time, I said, "Just put it on the desk."

There was a moment of silence; then, in a fidgety voice, the boy asked, "You got something I could put it in?"

— *Elaine L. Ericson*

"That allergy of hers will make medical history."